MOODY MARGARET STRIKES BACK

Francesca Simon spent her childhood on the beach in California, and then went to Yale and Oxford Universities to study medieval history and literature. She now lives in London with her English husband and their son. When she is not writing books she is doing theatre and restaurant reviews or chasing after her Tibetan Spaniel, Shanti.

Tony Ross is one of Britain's best known illustrators, with many picture books to his name as well as line drawings for many fiction titles. He lives in Nottinghamshire.

Complete list of Horrid Henry
titles at the end of the book

Also by Francesca Simon

Don't Cook Cinderella
Helping Hercules

and for younger readers

Don't Be Horrid, Henry
Horrid Henry's Birthday Party

MOODY
MARGARET
STRIKES BACK

Francesca Simon
Illustrated by Tony Ross

Orion
Children's Books

Moody Margaret Strikes Back originally appeared in
Horrid Henry versus Moody Margaret first published in Great Britain in 2009
by Orion Children's Books
This edition first published in Great Britain in 2010
a division of the Orion Publishing Group Ltd
Orion House
5 Upper St Martin's Lane
London WC2H 9EA
An Hachette UK company

A catalogue record for this book
is available from the British Library

Printed in Great Britain
by Clays Ltd, St Ives plc

www.horridhenry.co.uk
www.orionbooks.co.uk

CONTENTS

MOODY MARGARET'S SECRET CLUB

Naturally the Secret Club is the
best club ever. I'm the boss,
everyone does what I say, and
there are no boys allowed.
Henry and his stinky Purple Hand
Club are always
planning stupid
tricks and dares or
telling their UNfunny
jokes, but we can
outdo the boys any
day. After all we're
the ones who
stinkbombed the Purple
Hand and spiked their
drinks and booby-
trapped their entrance

1

and even stole their entire fort. HA!

HORRID HENRY:
Margaret doesn't know any good jokes, tricks or dares. Don't read her book – mine's much better!

Boys' jokes are NOT funny, but my jokes ABOUT boys definitely are.

What's the difference between a boy and a cowpat?
A cowpat stops being smelly after a couple of days.

Why did the boy take a pencil to bed?
To draw the curtains.

Why did the boy throw butter out of the window? Because he wanted to see a butter fly.

Rude Ralph made a rude noise in class. 'Stop that!' said Miss Battle-Axe.
'OK,' said Rude Ralph. 'Which way did it go?'

Doctor Dettol: Is your cough any better now?
Henry: It's much better, thank you. I've been practising for weeks.

Hey! Susan! You lazy lump! You're meant to be on the lookout. I just saw Henry sneaking around trying to spy on us.

SOUR SUSAN: I saw him. I am NOT a lazy lump!

I think that pongy pimple and his stupid club are up to something - and we need to find out what...

AN ENEMY
IN THE CAMP

Halt!
Who
goes
there?

SOUR
SUSAN:
It's the enemy. Send him back to
Henry's book.

PERFECT PETER: Can't I be in
your club? Henry is being horrid
to me. He won't let me join the
Purple Hand.

I don't want that little worm in
my club.

5

SOUR SUSAN: But maybe we could use him to spy on the Purple Hand.

I was just about to say that before you did.

SOUR SUSAN: Bossyboots.

Okay, Peter, we'll let you be in our club, if you tell us all your best tricks to outwit Henry.

PERFECT PETER'S TRICKS TO OUTWIT HENRY

- At night, wait until everyone's asleep, then creep downstairs and sleep there so you can take control of the TV remote first thing in the morning.

- Mess up Henry's room even more so that mine looks tidier than ever, Mum and Dad will reward me with extra pocket money, and punish Henry with no TV and no sweets for a week.

- Wrap up a piece of carrot in a  chocolate wrapper and leave it lying in the kitchen. Just watch Henry's face when he grabs the 'chocolate bar' and rips off the wrapper.

- Put blue food colouring in water or milk so that Henry will think it's a nasty, sweet drink and guzzle it all up.

- Ask Henry if you can test some new chocolate on him. Blindfold him and say, 'Open your mouth, and I'll pop it in.' When Henry is sitting with his mouth wide open, feed him a spoonful of prune yogurt.

Peter, now creep over to Henry's book, and find out what tricks he's planning to play on us.

SECOND IN COMMAND

When Peter comes back, let's give him some dares to do. Ha ha. Do you know any good ones?

SOUR SUSAN: If I tell you, will you promise to make me your Second in Command?

We'll see how good they are.

SOUR SUSAN'S DARES FOR PERFECT PETER

- Tell the bogey babysitter there's a creepy-crawly in her hair or climbing up her back. Watch her wriggle and scream!

- Put Henry's alarm on for four in the morning.

- If the babysitter sends you to bed too early, hide the remote, so that she can't watch TV all evening. Serves her right. Nah nah ne nah nah.

- In the middle of story time with Miss Lovely at school, give your best and loudest snort.

- Suck a slice of sour lemon, then try to whistle.

- When you've settled down to watch your favourite TV programme, *Manners with Maggie*, remove the batteries from the remote control so that Henry can't change channels to *Mutant Max*.

- While blindfolded feel a volunteer's face and see if you can guess who it is.

We can have loads of fun with that one. I'll blindfold Peter, and we'll get him to feel your face. Then while he's sitting there trying to think who it could be, we'll run off and hide.

- Eat a bowlful of Glop.

11

SOUR SUSAN: Am I Second in Command now?

Mmm, I might let Linda be Second. You can be Third. Unless you know any good jokes.

SOUR SUSAN'S JOKES

What do you call an insect who is always complaining?
A grumble bee.

How did the jockey talk to his pony?
In a hoarse voice.

Why won't oysters share?
Because they are shellfish.

Why are adults always complaining?
Because they are groan ups.

My mum lets me watch the TV all day.
Wow, I wish she was my mum.
No, you don't. She won't let me turn it on.

Oh, go on then. You can be
Second in Command.

NEW BEST FRIEND

Gurinder, do you want to be in my Secret Club?

GORGEOUS GURINDER: I don't know. I might join the Purple Hand Club instead. What's so good about the secret club?

We know all the best jokes and dares. Listen to these...

MORE OF MOODY MARGARET'S JOKES

Boy: I have three noses, five eyes and four mouths. What am I?
Girl: Very ugly.

Why was the boy upset when he won the prize for the scariest disguise at the Halloween party?
Because he only came to pick up his little sister!

Miss Battle-Axe: Henry, you scruffy boy, you've got holes in your trousers.
Henry: Of course I have. It's so I can get my legs in them!

Did you hear about the boy who put on a clean pair of socks every day?
By the end of the week he couldn't get his shoes on!

Miss Battle-Axe: Henry, if you had five pounds in one pocket and three pounds in another pocket, what would you have?
Horrid Henry: Someone else's trousers on.

Gurinder, you're a lot nicer than Susan and not so sour. If you join the Secret Club, you can be Second in Command if you like. And you can be my new best friend and come to my home for a sleepover.

SOUR SUSAN: Can I come?

No, you're not invited

SOUR SUSAN: That's not fair. She has got to do some dares first.

All right. You think up some good dares then.

SOUR SUSAN: Don't worry I will. You mean bossyboots.

What did you say?

SOUR SUSAN: Nothing (grouch).

SOUR SUSAN'S SLEEPOVER DARES FOR MOODY MARGARET

- Tie Gurinder's hair up in a silly-looking style, and make her keep it like that all the next day.

- Give Gurinder an amazing make-over, wearing a blindfold.

- Wait until Gurinder's asleep, then draw on her face with soap crayons or face paints and take some photographs to shock her with later.

- Mummify Gurinder using toilet paper.

- Scream in the middle of the night and wake her up.

SOUR SUSAN: Ha ha! Gurinder won't be Margaret's new best friend for long.

PERFECT PETER:
Margaret, I've got a
secret to tell you.
It's...

Go away, worm! Tell
me later. I'm busy.

MOODY MARGARET'S TOP TRICKS

Susan's dares are so mean, but they're still loads better than any of the boys' dares.

HORRID HENRY: You're wrong. Boys are best!

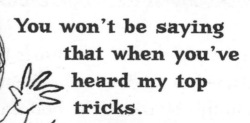

You won't be saying that when you've heard my top tricks.

MOODY MARGARET'S TOP TRICKS

- Tell all the boys Nurse Needle will be at school because it's injection day. Then sit back and watch Tough Toby tremble and Weepy William wail!

SOUR SUSAN: Henry's the worst. He's a great big crybaby.

I'll pretend to feel sorry for them – with my trick tissue box.

- Take out the top ten tissues from a tissue box, and sellotape them together. Do this by taking the bottom edge of one tissue and gluing it to the top edge of another tissue, until you've done them all. Then put them back in the box carefully, so that no one can tell there's anything odd about them. When one of the boys starts crying because he thinks Nurse Needle is coming, offer him a tissue – and make him look like a complete fool!

Ha ha! Here are some more tricks to get my own back on Henry.

• Knock on your next-door-neighbour's door, smile sweetly and tell them that your pet snake or tarantula is loose in their garden.

In my case, this means Henry.

- Hide Horrid Henry's favourite toy, Mr Kill. He can't sleep without it!

- Thread a piece of fine cotton through a five pound note, and place the note on the floor. When Henry sees it and tries to pick it up, pull the cotton away from him!

- When playing Henry's favourite board game, Gotcha, with him, make sure that you're the banker – and pinch lots of treasure from the bank when Henry's not looking. Then he'll be a loser every time!

HORRID HENRY: Margaret, Susan – I've got a dare for you.

HENRY'S DARE

• Don't laugh, giggle or even smile for one whole minute while everyone else tells you jokes and pulls funny faces.

MOODY MARGARET AND SOUR SUSAN: BAH! That is SO EASY!

Here's Clare. She'd make a great Second in Command. She's cleverer than Susan, and she'll know how to outwit Henry.

CLEVER CLARE'S TRICKS, JOKES AND DARES

CLEVER CLARE: Do you want to know some brilliant ways to make some money out of Henry?

MOODY MARGARET AND SOUR SUSAN: Yes please!

PERFECT PETER: Shall I tell you the secret now?

Not now. I told you to go away.

HOW CLEVER CLARE
TRICKS MONEY OUT OF
HORRID HENRY

🪙 Dare Henry to say the alphabet backwards. If he can, you have to give him a pound. But if he gets it wrong, he has to give you a pound.

CLEVER CLARE: I think I can safely say that Henry will be handing over a pound.

🪙 Say to Henry: 'I dare you to write with your toes on a piece of a paper.' Tell him that if he can do it, you'll give him a pound. If not, he owes you. When he's struggled unsuccessfully for a few minutes, produce another piece of paper that you prepared earlier. On the paper you have written 'with your toes'.

Tell Henry that you're not really clever and hardworking – but you're lucky enough to own a magic-homework-doing-pencil. Trick Henry into buying the pencil from you, and see how long it takes him to realise it's just an ordinary pencil.

 Offer to do Henry's homework for him – for a pound. But do it all wrong so that he still gets a rotten mark.

 Write Henry a fake sick note from his mum for school:

> *Dear Miss Battle-Axe*
>
> *Henry is ill, and will not be at school today.*
>
> *Henry's Mum*

Show it to Henry and tell him if he gives you a pound, you'll take it to school for him. Then quickly make a few changes!

Dear Miss Battle-Axe

pretending to be

Henry is ~~↓~~ ill, but he will ~~not~~ be at school today.

↑ still

Henry's Mum

Henry's going to be in such trouble at school. Nah nah ne nah nah!

CLARE'S CLEVEREST JOKES

What goes zzub zzub?
A bee flying backwards.

*What's bright orange and sounds
like a parrot?*
A carrot.

How do you make a pirate angry?
Take away the 'p' and he becomes irate.

*A frog went into a library. The librarian,
trying to be kind, offered it all sorts of books
to read.*
But the sulky frog didn't want any of
them — it just sat there saying 'reddit,
reddit, reddit.'

What do snakes learn at school?
Hiss-tory.

CLEVER CLARE'S FAVOURITE BOOKS

Easy Money by Robin Banks
Cliff Tragedy by Eileen Dover
The Hole in my Bucket by Lee King
Hungry Dog by Nora Bone
The Long Walk to School by Mr Bus

CLEVER CLARE'S RIDDLES

What has teeth but cannot eat?
A comb.

What gets wet the more it dries?
A towel.

What word is always spelled incorrectly?
Incorrectly.

*How many apples can you put in
an empty box?*
One. After that it's not empty any more.

CLEVER CLARE'S CLEVEREST TRICK

When your mum and dad have finished with their newspaper, hide it in your bedroom. When next morning's paper is delivered, sneakily swap the insides with yesterday's, leaving only the new front page. Watch to see if your parents notice that they are reading yesterday's news all over again!

You're so clever, Clare! You can be my Second in Command, if you like.

FIERY FIONA'S FUN

There's Fiona. Let's wind her up with some annoying tricks and jokes.

CLEVER CLARE: But let's tell her that they're all Henry's ideas. Then she'll be mad at him instead of us.

Good thinking. Hey Fiona, listen to Henry's jokes. I think he's trying to annoy you.

JOKES TO FIRE UP FIERY FIONA

What's Fiery Fiona's favourite food?
Scream cakes.

Why does Fiery Fiona ban whispering?
Because it's not aloud.

What kind of puzzle makes Fiery Fiona angry?
A crossword.

Knock knock
Who's there?
Boo
Boo who?
Don't cry, Fiona, it's only a joke.

33

FIERY FIONA:
Ha ha. Henry's
so horrible.

He told us
some tricks
too, and said
we should try
them out on you.

TRICKY TRICKS TO FIRE UP FIERY FIONA

- Make some tasty-looking biscuits, but sneak in some raisins. Offer one to Fiona and tell her that it's a chocolate chip cookie.

- Dare Fiona to fold a piece of paper up eight times. This will drive her crazy – because it's impossible.

- Say 'hippity hop' after anything you say to Fiona for ten minutes.

FIERY FIONA: Henry is so ANNOYING!

- Repeat everything Fiona says and copy all her actions. This is guaranteed to drive anyone mad – but especially Fiery Fiona.

- Take two eggs – one raw and the other hard-boiled, but keep that a secret. Tell Fiona you can make an egg stand on its rounded end and spin it like a top, but you bet that she can't. Give her the raw egg and watch her fail, while you show off with the hard-boiled egg. Ha!

- Dare Fiona to crumple up a double page of a newspaper, using only one hand. She won't be able to do it – and she'll get very angry trying!

- Make two pin pricks opposite each other near the bottom of a straw. Do the same at the top of the straw too. Give Fiona the straw with a glass of her favourite drink, and watch her struggle to slurp it up. The holes make it almost impossible for the drink to reach the top of the straw.

FIERY FIONA: AAAGH! I'm going straight round to tell Henry exactly what I think of him.

SINGING SORAYA SHRIEKS

SINGING SORAYA: I know some jokes and dares. Would you like to hear them?

As long as
she doesn't sing...
Go on then, let's
hear them.

SINGING SORAYA'S JOKES

How do you mend a tuba?
With a tuba glue.

What sort of music scares balloons?
Pop music!

Why did the girl sit on the ladder to sing?
She wanted to reach the high notes!

What musical key do cows sing in?
Beef flat.

Why did the man keep his trumpet in the fridge?
Because he liked cool music!

SINGING SORAYA'S DARES

• Stand on one foot and sing a song. But as soon as you're back on two feet, you have to stop singing.

• Try singing while you're doing the following:
  1. Holding a cup of water on top of your head and hopping.
  2. Balancing a spoon on your nose.
  3. Licking your elbow.

SOUR SUSAN: Even Soraya won't be able to sing very much if she's doing those dares!

- Eat a mouthful of crackers and then try to whistle.

I've got a dare for you, Soraya. Go over to the Purple Hand camp and sing as LOUDLY as you can. With all that racket - sorry, lovely singing - the boys won't be able to think of any good dares, tricks or jokes. And you can be my Second in Command in the Secret Club.

SINGING SORAYA: If my singing will help the girls and the Secret Club, I'll do it.

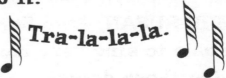

Tra-la-la-la.

THE WORM

PERFECT PETER: Please will you let me in your club? I'll tell you some really funny jokes.

PERFECT PETER'S JOKES

Patient: Doctor, Doctor, I keep thinking I'm invisible.
  Doctor: Who said that?

What's the best way to catch a rabbit?
Hide in the bushes and make a noise like lettuce.

Where do carrots eat their dinner?
At the veggie-table.

What's green and goes 'boing, boing'?
A spring onion.

**Terrible! I've got a better joke
than those.**

*How do you tell which end of a worm
is the head?*
Tickle him in the middle and watch
where he smiles.

**PERFECT PETER: Please, please
will you let me in your club? I've
got some good dares too.**

PERFECT PETER'S DARES

• Build a tower out of anything you can
  find until it is taller than you are.

• On your mum or dad's birthday, wrap yourself up as a birthday present.

That's terrible. Don't tell me any more.

PERFECT PETER: Please, please, please, let me in the club. You haven't even heard my secret yet.

Not now. Go back to
Henry's book and
stay there.

NEW NICK: I've brought you
some flowers, Margaret. I hope
you like them.

PERFECT PETER:
That's the
secret. There's
a w...

MOODY
MARGARET: Ooh,
thank you.

PERFECT PETER: Watch out! That's what I was trying to tell you. There's a w...

AAAAAGH!! Why didn't you tell me? Peter, you're a useless spy. Go home!

THE SECRET CLUB VERSUS THE PURPLE HAND

HORRID HENRY: Your silly Secret Club will never beat the Purple Hand with *those* useless dares and jokes.

Girls are cool and boys drool.

HORRID HENRY: We don't need a stupid rhyme like that to tell us boys are the best and girls are boring - nah nah ne nah nah!

Do some of my dares then. I dare you to sleep in a haunted bedroom.

HORRID HENRY: Easy-peasy. I dare you to hide under someone's bed and pretend to be a ghost by poking their mattress and twitching the duvet.

Okay, I'll do it to you! You'll

be screaming like a big baby.
Here are some dares for your
silly friends too.

DIZZY DAVE has to keep still for one
whole hour.

BABBLING BOB has to keep quiet for
one whole hour.

ANXIOUS ANDREW has
to sing in public for thirty
seconds.

RUDE RALPH has to
stand up every time Miss
Battle-Axe enters the
room, and call her 'Your
Majesty'.

TOUGH TOBY has to
go to school in his
sister's nightie.

Why did Greedy Graham eat his homework?
The teacher told him it was a piece of cake.

Why did Beefy Bert eat a £1 coin?
His mum told him it was for his dinner.

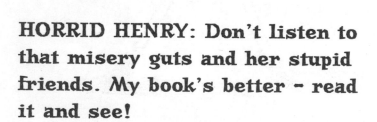

Mum: Do you like your new teacher?
Horrid Henry: No. She told me to sit at the front of the class for the present, and then she didn't give me one.

HORRID HENRY: Don't listen to that misery guts and her stupid friends. My book's better – read it and see!

That's got rid of him and all the other stinky boys. The Secret Club rules and my book is the best ever. Read on for the official top-secret results . . .

Top Secret Results

	SECRET CLUB	PURPLE HAND
DARES/TRICKS	100	-500
JOKES	100	-750

RESULT: The Secret Club wins!
The Purple Hand loses! Now it's your
turn to award points for the dares, tricks
and jokes in this book:

DARES/TRICKS ...../10

JOKES ...../10

GRAND TOTAL ...../20

When you've read *Horrid Henry's Double
Dare*, fill in your score for that book too.
Which book came out on top?

HORRID HENRY'S DOUBLE DARE ...../20

MOODY MARGARET STRIKES BACK ...../20

HORRID HENRY BOOKS

Once you've read all the Horrid Henry books,
why not see how well you know Henry and friends
and try the activity and puzzle books:

Horrid Henry's Brainbusters
Horrid Henry's Headscratchers
Horrid Henry's Mindbenders
Horrid Henry's Colouring Book
Horrid Henry's Puzzle Book
Horrid Henry's Sticker Book
Horrid Henry's Mad Mazes
Horrid Henry's Wicked Wordsearches
Horrid Henry's Crazy Crosswords

Visit Horrid Henry's website at
www.horridhenry.co.uk for competitions, games,
downloads and a monthly newsletter!